Raccoons

By Allan Fowler

Consultants
Linda Cornwell, Coordinator of School Quality
and Professional Improvement
Indiana State Teachers Association

Jan Jenner, Ph.D.

SCHOLASTIC INC.
New York Toronto London Auckland Sydney
Mexico City New Delhi Hong Kong

Designer: Herman Adler Design Group
Photo Researcher: Caroline Anderson
The photo on the cover of this book shows a young raccoon in the woods.

ISBN 0-516-23805-1

12 11 10 9 8 7 6 5 4   08   10 11 12 13 14 15/0

Printed in the U.S.A.

First Scholastic printing, March 2001

Have you ever worn a mask on Halloween?

A raccoon has black fur around its eyes.

It looks like it is wearing a mask.

A raccoon's fur is gray
or brownish gray.

It has a bushy tail with
black rings.

Raccoons are about
24 to 36 inches long,
including the tail.

Raccoons have five toes with sharp claws on each paw.

A raccoon uses its front paws like hands.

The red panda and the ringtail are close relatives of the raccoon.

Red panda

Two ringtails

Coati

The strangest relatives
of the raccoon are the
coati (ke-WA-ti) and the
kinkajou (KIN-ke-ju).

Kinkajou

13

Raccoons are good
swimmers.

They can also climb trees.

Most raccoons live in the forests of North and South America.

They build houses called dens in hollow trees, tree stumps, or logs.

Their homes are usually near a pond or stream.

Many raccoons live close
to cities or towns.

They may look for food
in gardens or garbage cans.

Raccoons usually hunt
at night.

Raccoons like to eat
mice, small birds, fish,
crabs, frogs, corn, fruit,
and insects.

Newborn raccoons

Young raccoons leave their den when they are about ten weeks old.

Then mother raccoons teach their young to hunt.

When the young are about a year old, they begin life on their own.

Words You Know

coati

den

kinkajou

mask

paw

ringtails

31

Index

About the Author

Allan Fowler is a freelance writer with a background in advertising. Born in New York, he now lives in Chicago and enjoys traveling.

Photo Credits

©: Animals Animals: 21 (Breck P. Kent), 29 (Zig Leszczynski); Comstock: cover, 17; Dembinsky Photo Assoc.: 26 (E. R. Degginger), 6 (Skip Moody); Peter Arnold Inc.: 11, 31 bottom (Kevin Schafer); Photo Researchers: 9, 31 top right (Ray Coleman), 22 (Phil A. Dotson), 10 (S. R. Maglione), 25, 30 top right (Leonard Lee Rue III), 13, 30 bottom (Jay Sauvanet); Stock Boston: 3, 31 top left (Paul Griffin); Visuals Unlimited: 5 (Ken Lucas), 12, 30 top left (Joe McDonald), 14 (Rob & Ann Simpson), 18 (Ron Spomer).

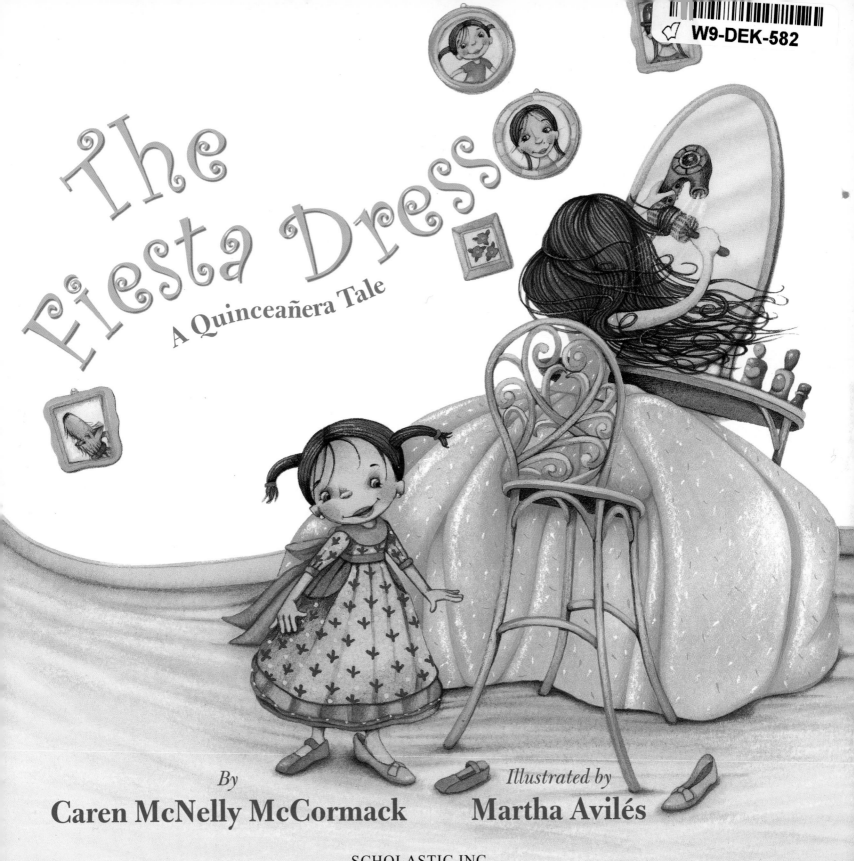

The Fiesta Dress

A Quinceañera Tale

By
Caren McNelly McCormack

Illustrated by
Martha Avilés

SCHOLASTIC INC.

ISBN 978-0-545-57266-8

12 11 10 9 8 7 6 5 4 3 2 1   13 14 15 16 17 18/0

Printed in the U.S.A.   08

First Scholastic printing, January 2013

The illustrations were rendered in acrylics
and liquid watercolor on Arches paper.
Book design by Vera Soki
Editor: Marilyn Mark

For Jon and J.C., both givers of good gifts
—C.M.M.

For Renata and Miranda
—M.A.

When you are the baby of the family everyone notices you.

Mamá and Papá clap when I pirouette my best ballerina twirls.

My big sister Eva cheers when I race to the end of the block.

The neighbors gasp when I climb to the top of the pecan tree before anyone can stop me.

"Lolo," Papá says, "you're always on the move."

"With fast feet like yours," Mamá says, "it's hard to keep up."

But while everyone prepared for Eva's *quinceañera*, no one noticed me.

The *damas* didn't as they swished and swirled in their bright dresses. They whirred, curled, brushed, and combed as they dressed for the *fiesta*. They never saw me patting clouds of powder on my face.

In the kitchen, no one noticed me. The *tías* didn't as they scooped, patted, wrapped, and tied, making the biggest batch of tamales ever. They never saw me slipping one into my pocket.

In the backyard, no one noticed me. The *tíos* didn't as
they unraveled, tossed, tugged, and twisted strands of lights
over the patio and through the trees. They never saw me
swinging from the pecan tree.

In the den, the *primos* didn't notice me. They huffed, puffed, whistled, and cheered at the video game. They never saw me practicing handstands against the wall.

Even Gobi, the *perro*, didn't notice me. He sighed, snuffled, scratched, and shook when I let him out of the laundry room. He flew past me and bounded upstairs before I could throw him his favorite squeaky toy.

But everyone noticed when—"AHHHH!"—Eva shrieked from the bedroom. The blow-dryers hushed. The pots piped down. The backyard lights fizzled. Even the video game clicked off.

"Gobi took my sash!" Eva screamed. "That drooling dog took my perfect white sash. My *quinceañera* dress is ruined!"

Mamá and Papá bolted to the laundry room.
"Where is that dog?" Papá moaned.
"How did Gobi get out?" Mamá wailed.
I gulped. I didn't want them to notice me now. I slipped out the door to look for Gobi.

I found Gobi at the corner with the sash in his clenched teeth.
"It looks like we're both in the doghouse," I said to him. "Give me the sash."
Gobi flicked his ears and clamped his teeth tighter.

"Come on." I popped my hands on my hips. I felt a lump in my pocket.
Aha! I knew just how to save Eva's sash.

"Who makes the best tamales on the planet?" I asked Gobi. I slid off the corn husk wrapper and dangled the tamale above him.

Gobi cocked his head.

"My *tías*!" I said and flipped the tamale into the air.

Gobi dropped the sash and leaped up for a bite.

Before his teeth closed on the tamale, I snatched the sash and dashed for home.

Mamá, Papá, and Eva met me
at the door.

"I'm sorry I let out Gobi," I said.
"I just wanted someone to play with me."

"You weren't using your head when you
opened the laundry room door," Papá said.

"But at least you used your head and your feet
to set the problem straight," Mamá said.

"I'm glad to have my sash back," Eva said as she brushed some dirt from my cheek. "But I'm even happier to have my special sister with me on my big day."

Eva pecked each of my cheeks. "*Besitos, besitos*," she said.

I beamed and spread my arms in a deep ballet bow.

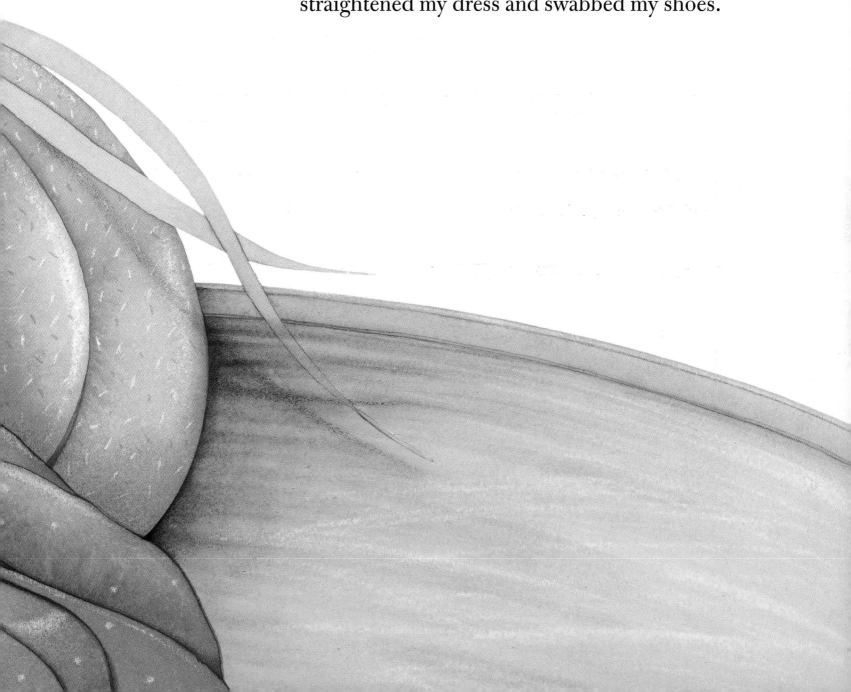

Then everyone noticed me.
The *damas* did. They swept me into Eva's room and twined my hair with ribbons. They straightened my dress and swabbed my shoes.

The *tías* noticed me. They hustled me into the kitchen and handed me the fattest tamale on a plate. They squeezed and kissed me while I ate by the stove.

The *tíos* noticed me, too. They whisked me to the
backyard and spun me in a *baile* under the twinkling lights.

They lifted me so I could swing from a high tree branch.

Even the *primos* clicked off the game in the den. They showered me with high fives and peppered me with questions.

And for the rest of the day, while everyone celebrated Eva's big *fiesta*,

Gobi and I whirled, munched, jumped, skipped, hummed, giggled, hollered, and grinned.

Glossary

Baile—Dance. *Quinceañera* parties often include special dances performed by the *quinceañera* girl and her attendants. After the choreographed dancing, the dance floor opens to all the guests.

Besitos—Kisses or, literally, little kisses

Damas—The *quinceañera* girl's female attendants, similar to bridesmaids. The *damas* are typically sisters, cousins, or friends. In a traditional *quinceañera*, fourteen *damas*, fourteen *chambelanes*, or male attendants, and a man of honor accompany the girl.

Fiesta—Party

Perro—Dog

Primos—Cousins

Quinceañera—Refers to both the girl and the event of the traditional celebration of a girl's 15th birthday held in many Latin countries and by Latinos in the United States. It marks a girl's change to womanhood. The *quinceañera* event has two parts: a Mass honoring the girl's commitment to the Church and a large party for friends and family. The party usually includes music and food and is held in a home or rented space. The *quinceañera* girl wears a full, formal dress, similar to a wedding gown, and her attendants wear colored formal gowns that complement the color of her dress.

Tías—Aunts

Tíos—Uncles